Positive Approaches
to Managing
Mental Ill Health

*A workbook to support the
mental health optional units
of the Certificates in
Working with People who
have Learning Disabilities*

JOHN BROOKE

Acknowledgements

The author is grateful to the course editorial and production team who supported the production of this workbook: Lesley Barcham, Sue Cowen, Tracey Tindell and Alison Wall.

British Library Cataloguing in Publication Data

A CIP record for this book is available from the Public Library

ISBN 1 904082 51 3

© Copyright 2003 BILD Publications

BILD Publications is the publishing office of the
British Institute of Learning Disabilities
Campion House
Green Street
Kidderminster
Worcs
DY10 1JL

Telephone: 01562 723010
Fax: 01562 723029
e-mail: enquiries@bild.org.uk
Website: www.bild.org.uk

Please contact BILD for a free publications catalogue listing
BILD books, reports and training materials.

BILD Publications are distributed worldwide by
Plymbridge Distributors Limited
Plymbridge House
Estover Road
Plymouth
United Kingdom
PL6 7PZ
Telephone: 01752 202301
Fax: 01752 202333

Contents

Introduction

Introduction

Welcome to *Positive Approaches to Managing Mental Ill Health*. This is a study workbook designed to provide the essential information for people undertaking the optional units of the Level 2 and Level 3 *Certificates in Working with People who have Learning Disabilities*. The workbook covers all of the learning outcomes for the level 2 unit *Contribute to the management of mental ill-health* and the level 3 unit *Help service users to manage mental ill-health*.

This workbook is one in a series of optional units from the LDAF *Certificates in Working with People who have Learning Disabilities* at levels 2 and 3, designed for staff in services supporting people with a learning disability. Units can be studied on their own or in groups or clusters. Each workbook covers all of the learning outcomes for the level 2 and 3 units.

Other workbooks in this series include:

- Induction – Learning Disabilities
- Foundation in Care – Understanding Abuse
- Foundation in Care – Understanding Positive Communication
- Eight study workbooks covering all of the mandatory units from both qualifications
- A series of six study workbooks on supporting people who present challenging behaviour
- Optional unit workbooks on autism, advocacy and palliative care.

It is possible to use this workbook:

- for your own personal study
- as part of an accredited learning programme, with a certificate to show what you have successfully learned (see page 7).
- to support in-house training or mentoring sessions.

Likely users

This workbook is aimed at:

- staff who have completed their induction and foundation units and are taking further units from the Level 2 or Level 3 Certificates

- more experienced staff working with people with a learning disability, who want to extend their skills and knowledge

- managers with responsibilities for staff supervision

- training managers in services for people with learning disabilities.

Staff members

This workbook will help you with your studies towards one of the optional units from the *Certificates in Working with People who have Learning Disabilities*. The book covers all of the learning outcomes for the unit. You can use the book as part of a distance learning course, to support in house training sessions or as part of supervision you may be receiving from a colleague or mentor. In addition to undertaking a programme of learning you will also need to complete assessment tasks to provide evidence of your learning. Your centre can arrange your assessment or BILD can assist with assessment of your work (for further information refer to the resources section at the end of this workbook).

Managers with responsibilities for staff supervision

This study workbook provides information and activities that you may find helpful in supporting staff in your service. It will be a useful resource in supervision sessions and should also be helpful for staff mentoring employees.

Training managers

If staff wish to use the learning they have completed in this workbook for accreditation towards the certificate, they need to be registered with one of the awarding bodies and studying on a recognised programme of study. They will also need to complete a portfolio of work for assessment. Further information on this can be obtained from BILD or the awarding bodies (see the resources section at the back of this workbook).

This workbook will be a useful resource for training managers planning and delivering units from the *Certificates in Working with People who have Learning Disabilities*. It can also be given to individual members of staff to:

- supplement training sessions

- consolidate learning

- assist learners in providing a portfolio of evidence, particularly for those seeking accreditation for their learning.

Relationship to other care qualifications

S/NVQ Qualifications in Care

Scottish/National Vocational Qualifications (S/NVQs) in Care and the level 2 and level 3 *Certificates in Working with People who have Learning Disabilities* are closely related qualifications. S/NVQs are related to National Occupational Standards and assess worker competence. The Certificates are Vocationally Related Qualifications (VRQs) and are a relatively new type of qualification that assess a learner's knowledge and some skills, but do not assess workplace competence. VRQs can provide a structured way for learners to gain the required underpinning knowledge towards an S/NVQ.

For further information on the relationship between S/NVQs and the *Certificates in Working with People who have Learning Disabilities*, go to the Learning Disabilities Awards Framework website at www.ldaf.org.uk.

Each unit from the two Certificates has been mapped to S/NVQ competences and can therefore be used to help learners acquire some of the underpinning knowledge towards an S/NVQ. Full details of the mapping for this unit can be obtained from the LDAF website www.ldaf.org.uk, from the Scheme Handbook for the Certificates or from the BILD assessment booklet for this unit.

Accreditation for your study

If you wish to receive accreditation for your study from this workbook, you will need to study on a programme provided by an organisation recognised by one of the awarding bodies (City and Guilds Affinity and National Open College Network) for the *Certificates in Working with People who have Learning Disabilities*.

BILD is one of the organisations recognised by the two awarding bodies – the City and Guilds and the National Open College Network. For more information about the BILD LDAF Programme, which provides in-house training, distance learning and supports satellite centres, please contact the Learning Services Administrator on 01562 723010.

Confidentiality and consent

An important aim of this workbook is to encourage you to relate what you are learning to your work situation. As part of this you will need to reflect on the way you work with people with a learning disability.

Before involving people with learning disabilities in any activities from this workbook, you need to make sure they understand what you are doing and obtain their consent. Discuss this with your line manager before going ahead. A few activities are based on discussions or observations of colleagues or people you support; when you write these up you need to be aware of the need for confidentiality. Never refer to anyone by their real name. Instead, always use an alias (a false name) or an initial to identify the person. Discuss your organisation's confidentiality policy with your line manager before completing any of the activities.

Labels and terms

There has been a great deal of debate about how to describe people with learning disabilities. Ideally we should call everyone by their names, since the most important thing to recognise is that each person is an individual, with a different personality, characteristics, strengths and failings. However, there are times when labels, no matter how much we dislike them, are used for all of us – student, parent, teenager, claimant, senior citizen, patient. Some labels carry negative connotations, some positive.

Throughout this workbook I use the term *learning disability*, which is the most commonly used term in health and social care settings. The terms 'mental handicap' and the American term 'mental retardation' are considered inappropriate and people with learning disabilities find them unacceptable. The term *people with learning difficulties* is preferred by the organisation People First which is run by people with learning disabilities. This term is also used in some education settings.

As you go through the workbook you will find I sometimes use the term service user to refer to people with learning disabilities, as they are the users of the service you work for. If you are studying this workbook, you're likely to be a paid member of staff, so I've generally used the terms *workers* or *practitioners*. However, much of the workbook content also applies if you are a volunteer or family carer.

I have also tried to avoid gender bias by using *he* or *she* alternately, except where this becomes clumsy or when I am referring to a particular person.

I use the word service to refer to your workplace situation, whether it is residential, day provision, based in the community or elsewhere. The word organisation refers to the agency that runs your service. Any other terms that may not be clear are explained as they arise.

How to use these materials

We all vary in how we study and in our learning patterns. Some people prefer to study in short bursts, spreading their learning over a long period. Others prefer more sustained periods of concentration. Some of us like to study early in the day; others don't start until later in the evening. No one way of studying is better than another. What matters is finding the way that suits you.

Whatever your preference, there are certain things you can do to make studying easier.

● Keep a pen or pencil with you while reading this workbook. Write comments in the margins or underline bits you find interesting or thought-provoking.

● Try to find a place for study where you will be undisturbed, and where you can leave your work safely.

● Plan a timetable that allows you to set aside time to study.

● Break the unit down into manageable chunks that you know you can complete in a set time.

● Keep your written work and any information you collect in a loose-leaf ringbinder.

● Discuss your study regularly with your line manager and colleagues. This will help you to think about how you can use the ideas from this workbook in your day-to-day support of people with learning disabilities.

These materials are interactive. As well as reading them, you will also need to:

● think about things

● give your own ideas and opinions

● talk to colleagues

● try out some activities.

There are different kinds of activities and you will need a pen and paper for some of them.

Unless learning is applied to your work, it is not very useful. So, throughout the workbook, summary 'Key Points' bring together the key ideas in the workbook and help you to put them into practice.

How this workbook is organised

There are three sections in this workbook:

1 Mental health and people with learning disabilities

This section looks at the differences between learning disabilities and mental health and why people with a learning disability are at greater risk of mental health problems.

2 Positive approaches to mental health

This section looks at ways of promoting good mental health and the social impact of mental ill health. The issue of consent to treatment is also covered.

3 Identifying and taking action on mental health problems

In this section the complexity of dual diagnosis is discussed and the responsibility of support staff in monitoring, recording and reporting mental health difficulties. The section also looks at the treatment and support available for people with mental ill health.

I suggest you do the workbook activities as you work through the materials. Doing these activities will help you to absorb the information and improve your work as a practitioner.

Good luck with your studying and enjoy the workbook!

SECTION 1:
Mental health and people with learning disabilities

Mental health and people with learning disabilities

The distinction between learning disabilities and mental ill health

The difference between learning disabilities and mental ill health is similar to the difference between any disability and any illness or disorder. An illness is usually treatable, and may be curable. A disability can be neither treated nor cured, although it may be possible to help a person with a disability to cope with it successfully. In some ways it is the difference between breaking your leg, and being born with one leg shorter than the other.

To fully understand the distinction between learning disability and mental ill health, we need to say what we mean by those terms. We will also look at the idea of mental health.

What is a learning disability?

A learning disability is not an illness. It is a major impairment of a person's ability to learn, to understand, to develop skills and to deal independently with the demands of everyday life. Learning disabilities emerge before adulthood, often at birth or soon after. They remain for life.

There is a wide and continuous range, or spectrum, from mild learning disabilities, through moderate, to severe and profound learning disabilities. Most people with mild learning disabilities manage well in society with help from family and friends. They may not need extra assistance, unless they run into additional problems such as mental ill health. People with more serious learning disabilities will often need lifelong specialist support of various kinds.

What is mental health?

You may already be familiar with the definition of health given by the World Health Organisation (1986):

Health is a state of complete physical, mental,
and social well-being, and not merely the
absence of disease or infirmity.

So we can say that mental health is:

- a state of mental well-being

- not just the absence of mental ill health

- part of our overall health.

This approach to mental health and to health generally looks at the whole person and the circumstances surrounding that person. It is often referred to as an holistic approach.

Our view of our own mental health is often very personal, or subjective. To someone who has experienced the severe mood swings of manic depression, even being in a constant low mood might seem like comparative good health. For another person, who has never experienced a mental health problem before, a mild depressive episode might appear as a frightening and serious illness.

These subjective views can depend not only on personal interpretations, but also on cultural differences which affect how people see mental health. Here are two examples.

- The eating disorder anorexia nervosa occurs mainly in Western societies and in young women. Many of them regard themselves as being in good mental health, although the condition may be causing physical and mental harm. What others regard as an illness is for them a way of coping with cultural demands to be slim and in control. Anorexia nervosa is almost unknown in cultures where a more rounded body shape is the ideal.

- People from some Asian cultures are reluctant to admit to depressive illness or its psychological and social symptoms. This seems to be linked to their unwillingness to discuss personal or family difficulties which may be part of the cause. Instead, they may tell doctors of aches and pains, or other physical problems.

What is mental ill health?

To turn the World Health Organisation definition of health on its head, we could say that mental ill health is a state of incomplete mental well-being. Something is wrong or missing in the mental skills and capabilities necessary to leading an ordinary life. In every culture, people are seen as having mental health problems if they cannot control their behaviour, care for themselves or carry out their social roles.

Like any other illness or disorder, mental ill health produces signs which can be observed by others, and symptoms which are noticed by the individual affected. These tend to group into three types of change in the person.

Mental changes
These affect thoughts, moods and feelings. For example, not being able to make sense of everyday happenings, a strong sense of sadness, or vagueness and an inability to cope with ordinary situations.

Physical changes
Among these are stomach upsets, palpitations, trembling and sweating heavily. Changes may also occur in eating, drinking, sexual activity and sleep.

Behavioural changes
Strange or bizarre actions, or behaviour not appropriate to the circumstances, may occur. Sometimes the person recognises the strangeness of the behaviour, but is not able to stop. Others will regard their actions as normal and reasonable, and not as a symptom of mental ill health.

There is no clear dividing line between mental health and mental ill health. It is best to think of the situation as a continuous link, or continuum, between good mental health at one end of the spectrum, and serious mental health problems at the other. Moving along the continuum usually takes time. When staff recognise the early stages of this, they can often take effective action to reduce the effects of mental ill health.

Activity 1: Differences between mental ill health and learning disabilities

The following differences are often used to distinguish between learning disability and mental health. Go through the list and tick one box for each to indicate which it applies to.

Difference	Learning disability	Mental ill health
1. Can occur at any age, but usually as an adult.	☐	☐
2. Affects learning and understanding.	☐	☐
3. Makes it difficult to learn living skills.	☐	☐

Difference	Learning disability	Mental ill health
4. Affects mental ability to lead an ordinary life.	☐	☐
5. Usually temporary, although perhaps long lasting.	☐	☐
6. Permanent and lifelong in its effects.	☐	☐
7. Often occurs at or near birth, and always before adulthood.	☐	☐
8. Affects feelings and thoughts and response to surroundings and other people.	☐	☐

Indicators for learning disabilities are: 2, 3, 6 and 7.

Indicators for mental ill health are: 1, 4, 5 and 8.

☞ *Key points*

Mental ill health is a state of incomplete mental well-being. Mental ill-health means an individual can experience mental, physical and behavioural changes.

Why people with learning disabilities are at greater risk of mental health problems

The risk of mental ill health is greater among people with learning disabilities than among the general population. Common mental health problems such as anxiety and depression occur more frequently among this group of people.

You will sometimes find this referred to as *a dual diagnosis of learning disability and mental ill health*, or simply as *dual diagnosis*.

Why do people with learning disabilities face a greater risk of mental health problems? To understand this, we need to look at the factors which make anyone more likely to have mental ill health, or predispose them to such problems. We can then consider which of them may particularly affect someone who has learning disabilities.

The term *factors* means the circumstances, influences, causes and situations which contribute to mental health problems. You may recognise a number of these from your own experience of working with people who have a dual diagnosis.

What factors predispose someone to mental ill health?

Just as health can be defined in terms of physical, mental and social well-being, so the risk factors which predispose people to mental ill health can be grouped in the same three categories.

Physical risk factors
- genetic inheritance through parents, eg possibly in schizophrenia and manic depression
- as a result of syndrome specific disorder eg Down syndrome, Fragile X syndrome
- some diseases, eg encephalitis
- head injury, eg in a road accident
- disorders of the nervous system, eg multiple sclerosis.

Mental risk factors
- various forms of abuse in childhood
- not having a stable family background
- rejection and neglect
- oppressive or authoritarian treatment.

Social risk factors
- adverse life events, eg bereavement;
- emotional difficulties, eg lack of a close relationship;
- isolation, eg a limited circle of friends.

All of these can help make it more likely that anyone will develop a mental health problem. Some of them affect people with learning disabilities more heavily. Some illustrations follow. As you go through them, reflect on your own experiences of working with people with learning disabilities, and try to think of other examples.

Additional physical factors

- Some physical factors in mental ill health arise from the same syndromes that cause learning disabilities. In people with Down syndrome there is a high risk of Alzheimer disease. Anxiety disorders are common among people who have Fragile X syndrome.

- Some conditions which occur more frequently among people with learning disabilities can pose additional risks. Epilepsy, although not itself a mental health problem, is linked with depression, anxiety and hallucinations.

- Brain damage, arising before or during birth or in early life, is both a cause of learning disabilities and a predisposing factor for mental ill health.

Additional psychological factors

- People with learning disabilities are more likely to be treated as inadequate, to be denied control of their lives, and to have low self-esteem. Oppression of this kind can lead to passivity and depression at one extreme, and to anger and aggression at the other.

- The unsettled and uncertain lives many people who have learning disabilities can expose them to a greater extent than other people to disruption, loss, separation and bereavement, and all the grief that comes with these.

- People with learning disabilities are more vulnerable to abuse, not only sexual and physical, but also mental and emotional. Often they will not possess the capacity to defend themselves, to ask for help, or to cope.

Additional social factors

- People with learning disabilities may have little in the way of family, friends or relationships in their lives. They are strongly disadvantaged in socially important areas such as education and work, and may have low status and little money. All this contributes to a sense of worthlessness and isolation.

- Communication is the "glue" of society. Inability to communicate with others in ways they can easily understand, or to understand them, adds to isolation, and tends to confirm other peoples' negative views.

- People with learning disabilities can be unfairly labelled, for example as stupid, comic or dangerous. This is sometimes called stigmatisation or stigma. It can add to feelings of low self-esteem and segregation.

Sonya feels rejected and alone.

Case study: Alice

Alice is a woman with Down syndrome. She was fortunate in having a stable family life and a good education when young. After the death of her parents, she spent a short time in a large residential home, then she moved to a hostel where she was unhappy, and finally settled in a staff-run bungalow with two other residents. She lived there contentedly for nearly ten years. In her mid-forties she began to have problems with short-term memory. Gradually she lost what had been previously good skills in dressing herself, handling money and carrying out household tasks. Her sense of time became poor, and her ability to concentrate weakened. When staff encouraged her to stick to tasks and complete them, she became distressed and, completely out of character for her, slightly aggressive.

The stability of Alice's early life helped her to cope with loss and bereavement. However, she now appears to have developed some form of dementia. Given that she has Down syndrome, this is probably linked to Alzheimer disease.

Activity 2: Describing factors which contribute to mental ill health

Using this case study as a guide, give an example of a service user you have worked with who has experienced mental ill health. Write a short account of what happened. Then describe the factors which you think may have contributed to the problem. Remember to keep the person anonymous by using a different name or an initial.

....

....

....

....

....

....

....

....

....

....

....

....

....

....

....

....

....

Comment

A person with a mental health problem remains first and foremost a person. The problem and its causes form part of that person's individual nature, and this applies to people with learning disabilities as much as to anyone else. When describing the causes and effects of mental ill health always try to focus on how they relate to the individual concerned.

☞ *Key points*

People with learning disabilities are more likely to develop mental ill health than the population as a whole. You should be able to describe the general risk factors for mental health problems, and identify which of them may particularly affect service users who have learning disabilities.

Common mental health problems

It is important that you should develop a basic knowledge of the common mental health problems, and of their main signs and symptoms. This is not as difficult as it sounds.

Activity 3, part 1: Naming common mental health problems

You will know of some of these through having heard or read about them. A few have already been mentioned in this workbook. You may have worked with people with learning disabilities who have a dual diagnosis of mental ill health.

From this existing knowledge, write down a list of common mental health problems. You can use technical terms, everyday expressions, or brief descriptions, whichever you prefer. There is no need to include signs and symptoms.

....

....

....

....

....

Comment

The aim of this activity was to start you thinking about what you already know of common mental health problems. It will also act as a baseline for you to look back to after you have completed part 2 of the activity at the end of this section.

Common mental health problems

Mental ill health in adults covers a wide range of conditions. The ones you are most likely to come across when working with people who have learning disabilities can be described under three headings:

psychosis
- psychotic states
- schizophrenia

mood disorders
- depression
- mania
- manic depression
- anxiety state
- obsessive/compulsive disorder

dementia
- different types of dementia
- Alzheimer disease

Signs and symptoms of mental ill health

As a member of staff, supporting someone with a learning disability who has a mental health problem, you may be involved in going with them to the doctor. Part of your work might involve:

- explaining to the doctor how that person communicates
- supporting the person to report his or her symptoms
- describing signs which you or others have observed.

To do this effectively, you will need to know the main signs and symptoms of the common mental health problems.

Psychosis

Psychotic states

These are a serious form of mental ill health. They can drastically alter the way in which a person sees the world, or even result in detachment from reality. Those who have the condition may not recognise their symptoms. The signs of psychotic illness are:

- impaired thinking and judgement
- strange and disruptive behaviour.

Schizophrenia

Around half of the people who produce signs of psychosis have schizophrenia. The main signs may include:

- disruptions in thought, eg switching abruptly from one topic to another
- hallucinations
- delusions
- changes in emotional response, eg becoming colder towards people
- changes in behaviour, perhaps becoming unpredictable, impulsive or aggressive.

Mood disorders

Depression

We all feel depressed at times. It is when the low mood is severe or prolonged that it becomes a mental health problem. Signs and symptoms may be:

- looking sad, tired and distressed
- loss of interest in life
- avoiding company
- poor self-image
- feelings of guilt
- sleep disorders, weight change.

Sonya is very depressed.

Mania

This is an abnormally high mood. Signs and symptoms are usually easily observed:

- restlessness, high energy and overactivity

- lack of direction in activities

- loss of inhibitions, eg overfriendliness

- sudden switches of mood, eg from pleasant to irritable.

Manic depression

Some people move between depression and mania in a cycle. You may hear this called *bipolar disorder*. The *poles* are low mood and high mood, and the person swings between the two.

Anxiety state

This can take a number of different forms. It includes phobias, such as fear of heights, insects or being out of doors. Sudden attacks are referred to as panic, and may occur regularly and follow a pattern. Someone who has an anxiety state may tell you of:

● difficulty in relaxing

● worry and unease

● a sense of doom or disaster.

Physical signs usually accompany anxiety:

● dizziness and trembling

● shortness of breath

● heavy sweating.

Obsessive/compulsive disorder

Most of us experience obsessions or compulsions at times. In obsessive/compulsive disorder these get out of control. The obsessive element refers to thoughts, which the person may tell you about:

● constantly recurring ideas

● persistent thoughts.

The compulsive element is the feeling that these ideas or thoughts must be acted on. This results in behaviour which is:

● irrational

● repetitive.

A person with obsessive/compulsive disorder might constantly be thinking about infection from dirt and germs, and seek to relieve this by repetitive and unnecessary hand washing.

Dementia

Different types of dementia

Dementia can arise from a number of causes. For some types, treatment can lead to improvement. Dementias related to alcohol abuse or hydrocephalus (pressure of fluid on the brain) are of this type. Other types of dementia lead to gradual or rapid deterioration or death. Examples are dementias arising from disorders of the nervous system such as multiple sclerosis, or from AIDS. Signs and symptoms of dementia include:

● problems with memory

● personality changes

● loss of reasoning powers

- disorientation and confusion
- decline in personal care and hygiene.

Alzheimer disease
This is an increasingly common cause of dementia, particularly among people who have Down syndrome. In its early stages it is difficult to detect other than by watching for gradual and permanent changes for the worse in:

- problem solving abilities
- reactions to what is happening around the person
- memory, beginning with the recent past
- behaviour and character.

Observable signs may include:

- aimless wandering
- eating less, with weight loss.

Activity 3, part 2: Signs and symptoms of mental ill health

For each of the following mental health problems, describe the signs and symptoms you would expect.

Obsessive/compulsive disorder

....

....

....

....

....

Depression

....

....

....

....

....

Dementia

....

....

....

....

....

Now read the following case studies, and state what type of mental ill health the service user might be developing.

Alan tells you he has been hearing voices in his head. Part way through this he abruptly begins to describe a recent visit to the seaside. You notice that he has begun to suffer from insomnia. Other staff have mentioned odd and unpredictable behaviour.

Alan is showing some signs and symptoms of ....

Nazra is typically quiet and pleasant, and good company. You notice she is beginning to look sad and exhausted. She avoids people she was friendly with, and gives up her amusements and interests. This is followed by episodes of unusually high mood, overactivity, and occasional irritation and suspicion. She seems to move from one extreme of mood to another with no obvious reason.

Nazra may be developing ....

Canaan has been worried and jumpy. When you chat to him, he begins a rambling explanation about something terrible which is about to happen. He cannot say what this disaster might be. You notice he is in a cold sweat, trembling, and labouring for breath.

Canaan's signs and symptoms suggest ....

Comment
Check your answers to the first part of this activity against the bullet points for signs and symptoms of these conditions given earlier in this section.

In the case studies:

- Alan is showing some signs of schizophrenia, or he may have some other psychotic state

- Nazra may be developing manic depression

- Canaan's signs and symptoms suggest an anxiety state.

Now go back to part 1 of Activity 3. Compare your awareness of common mental health problems now with when you began this section.

☞ *Key points*

Early detection of the signs and symptoms of mental ill health can help ensure that the needs of service users are properly met.

SECTION 2:
Positive approaches to mental health

Positive approaches to mental health

Ways of promoting good mental health

You will be accustomed to the ways in which health promotion can help people to keep or improve their physical good health. Efforts to persuade us to eat well, stop smoking, and exercise more are familiar to us all. You may well have used such methods in your work.

In the same way, mental health promotion can be employed to assist people to avoid mental ill health, reduce its effects, or to recover from it. Because people with learning disabilities are more vulnerable to mental health problems, it is important that staff who support them are familiar with the key methods for promoting good mental health:

- reducing stress
- building positive self-esteem
- talking and other communication
- giving control
- reducing isolation
- evaluating mental health promotion.

Reducing stress

We all experience stress and know how it feels. But we might find it difficult to give a short definition. Some stress is inevitable, and may be good for us, for example as a motivation to get things done. Too much stress, however, is damaging mentally and physically. Stress which goes on too long, or at a level we cannot cope with, is a health risk.

The way people with learning disabilities are treated in our society can seriously raise their stress levels. Some methods staff can use to help them reduce this are:

- cutting down on frustration, eg by helping people to achieve goals, or to recognise that they are unrealistic
- maintaining some regular patterns in life, eg with sleep, and some mealtimes and activities
- making events more predictable, and avoiding unexpected shocks
- giving people more control over what happens in their lives.

Building positive self-esteem

Self-esteem is about how much we approve of ourselves. We all have an idea of the person we are, and of the person we would like to be. When the gap we perceive between the two is narrow, our self-esteem will be positive. This is good for mental health. If there is a wide gap, this creates negative or low self-esteem, makes us feel bad about ourselves, and increases the risk of mental ill health.

People with learning disabilities are often made to feel that there is a huge divide between what they are and what they should be. Staff can support them to build positive self-esteem by helping them to:

- avoid situations where they are bound to fail, or look inadequate
- set realistic but challenging goals, and get the support needed to achieve them
- develop abilities and skills which they and others value
- lead lifestyles which they and people in their community see as worthwhile.

Talking and other communication

We all know how good it can feel to talk a problem through with someone. People with learning disabilities frequently rely on staff for this. Nor is talking the only way to communicate. Body language and ways of listening are important. Especially where mental health problems are involved, you may have to learn from the service user how he or she wants to communicate before you can begin.

Be aware of your own and the other person's body language:

- posture and body position
- facial expressions
- eye contact
- gestures.

Useful skills are:

- opening up a conversation
- prompting someone to express his or her feelings
- actively listening, not just hearing
- knowing when silence helps.

Sonya gets the chance to talk about how she feels.

Giving control

People are entitled to a say in the major decisions which affect their lives. But many people with learning disabilities find that the real control in their lives is in the hands of others. This leads to feelings of conflict, frustration and helplessness, which can result in mental health problems such as anxiety states and depression.

Staff can give control to service users by:

● providing information about choices, opportunities and alternatives

● enabling them to state their preferences and decisions

● supporting access to independent advocacy of different kinds

● ensuring that choices and decisions are not forgotten or ignored.

Reducing isolation

Even when living in the community, people with learning disabilities can be cut off from others by physical barriers, attitudes, or lack of opportunity. Physical barriers can be the location of someone's home, transport problems, or not being able to use a wheelchair because proper provision has not been made. Attitudes towards people with learning disabilities can mean individuals feel unwelcome, out of place, or excluded. Restricted lifestyles may deny people with learning disabilities opportunity to make contacts, develop friendships, or build relationships.

Staff can tackle isolation by:

- using available transport to best advantage
- supporting service users to complain about poor access to community facilities
- supporting activities which are part of community life
- enabling people to keep in touch with family and old friends
- helping to widen circles of new acquaintances and friends.

Evaluating mental health promotion

Not all methods for promoting good mental health are suitable for everyone, and individual needs may change with time. It is important to keep an eye on the results of your efforts to promote mental health. You can then continue with the methods which work for a particular individual, and change or replace other approaches.

This process of evaluation should be carried out on a regular basis, depending on the needs of the service user.

People who should be involved in evaluation include:

- the service user
- the service user's keyworker
- any advocate or self-advocacy supporter
- family and friends
- professionals involved, eg staff, GP, therapists.

To carry out an evaluation, you will need:

- a baseline record of the service user's previous mental health
- a record of the mental health objectives set
- a report on the service user's present mental health, and how far objectives in health promotion have been achieved.

By comparing the baseline and objectives with the current position, you will be able to evaluate the degree of success. If the goal was to prevent an early stage of anxiety state from worsening, then no change would be a positive achievement. If the aim was to lessen the effects of severe depression, changes for the better in the signs and symptoms of the condition would represent progress.

Activity 4: Promoting good mental health

Think of a service user, if possible one who has had mental health problems.

Can you think of an example of each of the following for that person?

	Yes	No
Reducing stress	☐	☐
Building positive self-esteem	☐	☐
Talking through problems	☐	☐
Giving control	☐	☐
Reducing isolation	☐	☐
An assessment of mental health	☐	☐
Objectives for mental health	☐	☐
Evaluation of mental health promotion	☐	☐

Comment
If all the answers are "yes", it is likely that the service user you are thinking about is receiving effective mental health promotion. The more you have answered "no", the greater the possibility that you need to give more attention to this aspect of care.

☞ *Key points*

The key methods for promoting good mental health include:
• reducing stress
• building self esteem
• talking and other communication
• giving control
• reducing isolation.
You should identify and use methods suitable to the individual involved and regularly evaluate their effects.

The social impact of mental ill health

Many of the factors which predispose people to mental health problems are social. In turn, mental ill health causes social problems for individuals. A vicious circle can develop, with social risk factors leading to mental ill health, and mental health problems worsening social risk factors. Part of the role of staff is to aid service users to break free of this pattern, and maintain their social well-being.

What is social well-being?

This varies from person to person, but most of us would include the following:

- contact and involvement with other people
- a valued and respected role in society
- a safe and pleasant place to live
- control over one's way of life.

Social impact of mental health problems

A double diagnosis of learning disabilities and mental ill health is likely to have a double impact on social well-being. Three aspects in particular may cause difficulties:

- stigma
- relationships
- lifestyle.

Stigma

People find mental ill health disturbing and frightening. A label is attached to someone with mental health problems which can make him or her less valued and respected, and someone to avoid. The label is often permanent, remaining attached even when the individual recovers good mental health.

Relationships

People do not invite those with mental health problems to join in. They may actively seek to keep them out. This can be made worse if staff and the families of those with mental ill health overprotect them, and keep them out of mainstream life.

Lifestyle

Mental ill health can affect where an individual lives, and who with. It can damage educational and work prospects. It can limit control over one's life, and can reduces opportunity and choice.

Reducing social impacts of mental ill health

Staff can use their own social skills to make a major difference to the social well-being of service users with mental health problems. Some approaches which have been found effective are to:

- avoid overprotecting the person, or "wrapping them in cotton wool"

- encourage the person to go out to social activities in the community

- be available to offer a chat or company when needed

- help the service user to communicate with other people

- broaden the service user's social contacts

- show personal respect, and value the individual.

Case study: David

David is a young man who lives in a residential home not far from his family, and in the area where he was brought up. He is being treated for manic depression. His switches of mood, from cheerful friendliness to suspicion and aggression, have frightened and angered his family and local people. Many of his favourite social activities, such as going to coffee shops to meet friends, have now been dropped. This seems to make his condition worse.

Activity 5: Minimising the social impact of mental ill health

List four interventions you would consider using to reduce the social impact on David of his mental health problems.

....

....

....

....

....

Comment
Your interventions should focus on what you know of David's strengths and needs. Strengths are his family and friends, his interests, and his role in the community. His needs are to keep these in his life, despite his problems.

Interventions should include:

- explaining David's problems to his family and friends
- talking things through with David
- encouraging him to keep up his usual social activities
- providing extra staff support for these activities.

☞ *Key points*

You need to be alert to the negative effects of mental ill health on the social well-being of a service user. You should be aware of and use a variety of methods to reduce these social impacts.

Seeking a service user's consent to treatment

You work with a woman who has learning disabilities. A mental health problem has been diagnosed. Her doctor recommends treatment. It seems obvious that this should go ahead. Then you remember how much effort has been put into giving this woman control of her life, and how positive the effects have been for her. Surely this applies just as much to medical treatment?

You are right. It does. You have just raised the highly important question of consent.

Why seek consent to treatment?

There are two good reasons to seek consent to treatment:

- health care ethics says you should
- the law says you must.

Health care of all kinds is based on ethical principles. A central principle of ethics is that we have the right to run our own lives and make our own decisions. Each of us has the right, in normal circumstances, to accept or refuse medical treatment.

The law is quite clear. Before a doctor, nurse or other healthcare professional gives treatment to a competent adult, you must obtain that person's informed consent. We will look at what precisely is meant by these terms, and at some exceptions. But generally that is the position.

The law is slightly different for children, and in Northern Ireland and Scotland. We will look at these differences at the end of this section.

How to seek consent to treatment

The following steps must be taken to ensure valid consent to treatment is obtained to examination, treatment and care. This includes by implication consent to diagnosis, which involves the examination of an individual's signs and symptoms. These steps are taken from the Department of Health guidance on the subject, which should be consulted if there is any doubt. The following steps are taken from the Department of Health (2001) guidance on this subject.

● Adults are assumed to be competent to give or refuse consent, unless it can be demonstrated otherwise.

● If there is doubt about competence, the question to be answered is: "Can this service user understand and weigh up the information needed to make this decision?"

● A service user may be competent to make some decisions, but not others.

● Wherever possible, consent should be asked for by the person who will treat the service user.

● The service user must be given as much information as is reasonably needed to decide on consent, and this must be in a form he or she understands.

● Consent must be voluntary, and not given under any pressure from staff, family members or others.

● Consent can be given in writing, in speech, or in non-verbal form. Your organisation may have rules about how it is recorded.

● Competent adults can refuse consent, even if treatment would benefit their health. They do not have to give a reason.

There is one exception to the right to refuse treatment by a competent adult. This applies where treatment is for a mental health problem, and the service user is detained under the Mental Health Act 1983. Under this legislation, the right to refuse can be removed. But there are extra safeguards, including second opinions from doctors, and rights to appeal.

Sonya has medical treatment for depression explained.

Adults who are not competent

If a service user cannot understand or weigh up the information needed to make a decision, then he or she is not competent to make that decision. Even then, no one else can give consent on that person's behalf. But it may be possible to give treatment in that person's best interests.

Deciding on someone's best interests is not a matter of thinking: "This will make him feel better, so it's all right."

Before medical staff can make a decision to give treatment in the best interests of an adult who is not competent, they must consult with those who are close to that person. They are required to take into account the service user's:

- needs and well-being
- wishes and preferences when competent
- religious and spiritual welfare
- cultural background and beliefs.

Children and consent to treatment

Young people aged 16 and 17 must be assumed competent to decide for themselves, unless demonstrated otherwise. Younger children who fully understand what is involved in treatment can also give consent, although ideally their parents will be involved. Otherwise, someone with parental responsibility must give consent.

Consent in Northern Ireland

At present (2002), the position in Northern Ireland on giving consent to treatment reflects the situation in England and Wales. The *Mental Health Act 1983* applies in Northern Ireland.

Consent in Scotland

In Scotland, the situation is now more straightforward. The *Adults with Incapacity (Scotland) Act 2000* introduces three important provisions.

- Staff giving day-to-day care to people who have been assessed as lacking capacity to give consent have authority to act reasonably in providing that care. This covers, for example, helping people with activities of daily living without formal consent.

- Emergency treatment can be given where consent cannot be obtained. For example, when someone is unconscious or incapacitated.

- The Department of Health guidance described earlier in this workbook will be given the weight of law, including the rules on consultation.

Activity 6: Your organisation's procedures on medical consent

Obtain a copy of your organisation's policy and procedures on seeking consent to treatment. If you do not know where this is kept, ask your manager.

Read through the policy, using the guidelines given earlier in this section.

Does the policy conform with those guidelines?

Do you understand the steps you need to take to seek consent to treatment?

Do you know how your organisation requires you to record consent to treatment?

Comment

If you find any points about which you are unclear in the policy and procedures, write notes on these. As soon as you can, make an appointment to discuss them with your manager.

☞ *Key points*

Whenever possible, a service user's informed consent to treatment of mental ill health must be obtained and recorded. Staff are responsible for knowing and using their organisation's procedures for this.

SECTION 3:
Identifying and taking action on mental health problems

Identifying and taking action on mental health problems

Monitoring, recording and reporting mental health

When working with service users who have mental health problems, you should at regular intervals check to see if their condition has changed. This is monitoring.

Monitor comes from a word meaning to warn, which tells us why this process is important. It gives warning of any worsening of mental ill health.

What signs should be monitored?

You now know the signs and symptoms of the more common mental health problems. These should always be noted and reported.

However, signs of mental health problems in people with learning disabilities can sometimes look different. Also, a service user may not recognise or be able to describe symptoms. Because of this, staff should look out for any significant changes in four key areas:

- mood and emotions
- behaviour
- level of awareness
- physical well-being.

Mood and emotions

Are emotional reactions to people or events different? Are there signs of feeling low, anxious or afraid? Has a person's self-esteem dropped? Can changes in mood be explained, for example by an upsetting incident?

Behaviour

Are there problems in getting on with people? Has there been any loss of skills? Are levels of activity very much higher or lower? Have new behaviours emerged?

Level of awareness

Are there signs of confusion or disorientation? Is there memory loss? Does the service user take an interest in what is going on around?

Physical well-being

Has there been any change in appearance? Are there changes in functions such as eating and drinking, bowel movements, sleeping? Have self-care and hygiene declined?

What are the procedures for recording and reporting?

Some general points should be kept in mind.

- Monitoring should not seem like spying. Tell the person being observed what you are doing and why. He or she should be encouraged to take part by talking to you about symptoms experienced.

- Your task is to observe, record and report. At this stage, you are not trying to diagnose mental ill health, although your records will contribute to this process later on.

- Changes in mental health can be slow and come in small steps. It may take careful observation over time to pick them up. Monitoring should be a regular activity.

All organisations have their own procedures for monitoring, recording and reporting on the physical and mental health of service users. Staff should be familiar with these. They are often based on instructions for the completion of records, and how to bring these together to be analysed for indications of any emerging problems.

Activity 7: Your organisation's procedures for monitoring, recording and reporting

Find out from other staff or your manager where details of your organisation's procedures on this are kept.

Describe these procedures in answer to the following questions.

What are the instructions for monitoring health?

....

....

....

....

What method is used for recording observations?

....

....

....

....

....

How are observations reported?

....

....

....

....

....

Who are the staff responsible for acting on observations?

....

....

....

....

....

Comment

It is important that staff understand their duties and responsibilities for observing and taking action on signs of mental ill health. If, after this activity, you are unsure about any aspect of monitoring and recording health, ask your manager about it.

☞ *Key points*

It is important to monitor signs of possible mental ill health in service users. This should be done in line with the procedures of your organisation relating to the recording and reporting of observations.

The complexities of dual diagnosis

Where learning disabilities and mental ill health occur together, this can cause additional difficulties with:

● accurate diagnosis of mental health problems

● access to mental health services

● labelling and stereotyping.

Difficulties in diagnosis

It can be difficult to get to the facts needed for diagnosis of mental health problems in someone who has learning disabilities.

● The problem may not be one of mental ill health, but something else. For example, bizarre behaviour may be caused by physical factors such as sleep disorders, pain or epilepsy. A person who has learning disabilities may not understand or be able to tell you about these.

● Signs of a problem with mental health may be put down to the person's learning disabilities.

● In people with learning disabilities, a mental health problem can present different signs and symptoms. This is known as *atypical presentation*. Schizophrenia might first be seen in withdrawal, anxiety and fear, and severe sleep disturbances, rather than the typical signs.

● The service user may not be able to describe experiences or feelings in ways others will recognise. Sometimes a person's already limited communication skills are worsened by mental ill health.

Diagnosis and assessment tools

Diagnosis of mental health problems is a complex process, carried out by psychiatrists and psychologists. As part of this they employ lists of questions, signs and symptoms, and other information to be gathered. These are known as assessment tools.

Most assessment tools derive from the two internationally recognised systems for classifying ill health: the Diagnostic Statistic Manual (DSM) and the International Classification of Diseases (ICD). These are periodically updated, and you will hear them referred to by their latest revisions, DSM IV or ICD 10.

Because of the complexities of dual diagnosis, mental health assessment tools have been designed specifically for people with learning disabilities. Doubts have been expressed about the reliability and accuracy of some of these.

The Psychiatric Assessment Schedule for Adults with Developmental Disabilities (PAS-ADD) was developed in 1993 to improve detection and diagnosis of mental ill health in people with learning disabilities. It is based on interviews with service users, and with people who may have key information, such as families and care staff. The tool is for use by psychiatrists and psychologists who are trained in clinical interviewing.

There are two modified versions of PAS-ADD. The Mini PAS-ADD is for qualified nurses and social workers who have had training in its use. It is based on information collection rather than interviews. The PAS-ADD Checklist is a short schedule for use by care staff and families. It can be helpful in deciding whether further assessment is needed. Both versions can make substantial contributions to diagnosis as part of the PAS-ADD process.

PAS-ADD and other assessment tools form only part of a wider assessment process, which may be in several stages. Diagnosis of mental health problems, especially in people who have learning disabilities, is a complex and often lengthy affair.

Accessing mental health services

Once someone with learning disabilities is diagnosed as having a mental health problem, that person's needs for care and treatment are the same as for anyone else in that position. But it can be difficult to gain access to the necessary service provision because of:

- generally inadequate mental health services for people with learning disabilities

- insufficient knowledge in learning disability services about the availability of mental health services

- reluctance by some mental health services to accept people with learning disabilities

- lack of resources and skills in mental health care in learning disability services.

To get round these obstacles it is essential that mental health and learning disability services work closely together. Staff in both services have a central role to play in ensuring that people with dual diagnosis get the treatment they need for mental ill health.

Labelling and stereotyping

Where someone has a dual diagnosis of a learning disability and mental health problems, then both labels are likely to be attached. This greatly increases that person's chances of being badly treated, discriminated against and excluded.

Part of the problem is the tendency to see people as stereotypes. This word comes from printing, where it describes a plate which always reproduces exactly the same words or images. People, of course, are not like this. They are always changing, and showing new sides to themselves. But the moment someone is said to have a learning disability or mental ill health, many people form a fixed image. This will always be negative, and often very hard to change.

Activity 8: Working with dual diagnosis

Think of a service user with learning disabilities who has, or may have, a mental health problem. Remember the issue of confidentiality when completing this activity.

Using your knowledge of this service user, go through the following steps.

Establish a baseline
Describe the person's usual behaviour, appearance, pattern of moods, level of functioning and awareness etc.

....

....

....

....

....

Look for changes
Remember the idea of a continuum from mental health to ill health. Identify changes from your baseline description.

....

....

....

....

....

Look for a pattern

Do the changes, the signs and symptoms, make up a pattern? Does this pattern suggest a mental health problem?

....

....

....

....

....

....

Look for alternative explanations

Could the changes indicate adolescence, the menopause, or ageing? Are they signs of a physical health problem? Are they a response to circumstances or events?

....

....

....

....

....

....

Avoid jumping to conclusions

Dual diagnosis is complex. Often we cannot be sure of the answers to these questions. If that is so, be open and honest about it. Are there still ways to offer support and help to the service user?

....

....

....

....

....

....

Comments
Remember that if you are unsure about the mental health of a person with a learning disability that you work with that you should seek professional medical advice and support. The individual should consent to any diagnostic tests and treatment that they receive.

☞ *Key points*

Dual diagnosis of a learning disability and mental ill health is complex. Staff should be aware of the difficulties, and of the steps they can take to ensure that service users' mental health needs are identified and met.

Treatment and support for mental ill health

A person with learning disabilities should be able to access the same mental health services as anyone else. These will include:

● specialist assessment and diagnosis

● medical treatment

● psychological therapies

● counselling

● social support

● mental health education.

Services are available through a number of different organisations and individuals. Most will be open to anyone with a mental health problem, and are known as generic services. Some may be specialist services for people with learning disabilities. Staff should work closely with generic and specialist services to encourage a team approach to dual diagnosis.

Organisations
The following organisations can provide information and advise on mental health issues:

● Mental Health Foundation

● MIND (National Association for Mental Health)

● National Schizophrenic Fellowship

● Richmond Fellowship

● Samaritans

● UKAN (United Kingdom Advocacy Network)

Individuals

The following individuals can provide information and advise on mental health issues:

- Clinical psychologists

- Counsellors

- General Practitioners (GPs)

- Mental health nurses

  in hospitals

  in day centres

  community psychiatric nurses (CPNs)

  dual qualified nurses

- Psychiatrists

- Specialist social workers.

Many of these individual professionals can be contacted through local medical centres, NHS trusts, and social services departments.

Activity 9: Finding out about treatment and support

Choose one organisation and one type of professional about which you know little.

Make enquiries and write brief notes about each under the following headings.

Local representation and projects

....

....

The people involved locally

....

....

How to contact them

....

....

What treatment or support they offer

....

....

Links to other services

....

....

Comment
The information you gain will be useful in care planning, and in dealing with crises. You and your colleagues might find it useful to have similar information to hand on all local sources of treatment and support.

Measuring outcomes of treatment

Once diagnosis has been carried out and treatment started, it is important to know if the results are effective and beneficial to the mental health of the individual. If not, the medication or support given will need to be changed. Just as there are assessment tools to help with diagnosis, so rating instruments have been developed to measure the outcomes of treatment.

An example of such an instrument, which is widely accepted for reliability and validity, is the Health of the Nation Outcome Scales for People with Learning Disabilities (HoNOS-LD). As its name indicates, this is part of a wider range of tools for use with all people with mental health problems, but one which has been specifically designed to be helpful with individuals who have a learning disability as well.

HoNOS-LD measures change in an individual over two or more points in time. At each point a standard form is completed in line with strict guidelines. This can be done on paper, or using a computer programme. A record is made of the person's rating in relation to 18 different factors, including behavioural problems, anxiety, mood changes, self-care, etc. The forms are completed by psychiatrists, psychologists, or behavioural support workers such as nurses.

By comparing the presence or severity of problems at different times, a picture emerges of whether or not the approaches adopted to someone's mental health problems have helped. For example, following diagnosis with a tool such as PAS-ADD, someone might be offered anger management therapy. A HoNOS-LD rating could then be carried out when the therapy starts, and again four weeks later. If there are signs of improvement, this would suggest the therapy should continue as it is. If there is no change or a deterioration, then a different approach, perhaps medication to support the therapy, may be indicated. The rating instrument can also assist in deciding when the outcome of treatment has been sufficiently successful for it to be reduced or withdrawn.

Barriers to accessing treatment and support

We have already looked at some of these barriers when examining the complexities of dual diagnosis. Some arise from deficiencies in services, and others from the need for more training or experience to be offered to staff. By studying this workbook, you have increased your knowledge and skills, and have contributed to improving the situation.

An additional obstacle can sometimes be staff worries about returning to the old medical model for learning disabilities. This is understandable. A learning disability is not an illness, and should not be treated as one. But people with learning disabilities can become ill, just like anyone else. This includes the possibility of mental ill health. When that happens, appropriate medical treatment is an entitlement.

Barriers to treatment can be raised by labelling, stereotyping and stigmatisation. Support staff need to know how to challenge negative attitudes and uphold the dignity and rights of individuals with a learning disability.

Staff who support people with a dual diagnosis must ensure that necessary treatment is not denied because of these factors. This may involve assisting other health professionals to distinguish between the effects of a person's learning disability and signs of mental health problems.

Finally, access to mental health services can be obstructed by lack of information. Staff should make sure that they are aware of the local mental health services, treatment and support available to service users.

Helping service users overcome barriers to treatment

This will involve using what you have learned from this workbook in your work. Everything you have studied has a practical application in supporting people with learning disabilities who develop mental ill health to get the treatment they need.

Now you have completed the workbook, take time to reflect on the ground you have covered. Think about how your new knowledge and skills can be put to use in meeting the mental health needs of the people with learning disabilities you support. Use the topics we have examined as a guide.

- The distinction between learning disabilities and mental ill health
- Mental ill health in people with learning disabilities
- Signs and symptoms of common mental health problems
- Ways of promoting good mental health
- The social impact of mental ill health
- Seeking a service user's consent to treatment
- Monitoring, recording and reporting mental health
- The complexities of dual diagnosis
- Treatment and support for mental ill health

☞ *Key points*

Mental ill health is usually treatable, and often curable. People with learning disabilities are more vulnerable to mental health problems, but they can be helped to recover from them. Staff who have been trained to support service users with a dual diagnosis can play a key role in their recovery.

Sonya is encouraged to keep up activities she enjoys.

SECTION 4:
Resources

Resources

Carpenter D, Turnbull J, Kay A (1996) *Mental Health and Learning Disability.* London: Macmillan

Costello T W, Costello J T, Holmes D A (1995) *Abnormal Psychology.* London: Harper Collins

Department of Health (2001) *12 Key Points on Consent: the law in England.* London: Department of Health

Gates B (1997) *Learning Disabilities: A Handbook of Care.* Edinburgh: Churchill Livingstone

Harris J, Simpson N, Rodgers J (2000) *Better Health: Improving Health Promotion and Health Care for People with a Learning Disability.* Kidderminster: BILD

Kerr M, ed. (1998) *Innovations in Health Care for People with Intellectual Disabilities.* Chorley: Lisieux Hall Publications

Moss S (2002) *The Mini PAS-ADD Interview Pack – Psychiatric Assessments. Schedules for Adults with developmental Disabilities.* Brighton: Pavilion Publishing

O'Hara J, Sperlinger A, eds. (1997) *Adults with Learning Disabilities: A Practical Approach for Health Professionals.* Chichester: John Wiley & Sons

Roy A, et al (2002) *HoNOS–LD: Health of the Nation Outcome Scales for People with Learning Disabilities.* Kidderminster: BILD

World Health Organisation (1986) in Gillian R (1986) *Philosophical Medical Ethics.* Chichester: Wiley and Sons

Organisations

City and Guilds Affinity (Awarding body)
1 Giltspur Street
London EC1A 9DD
Tel: 020 7294 2800
Email: enquiry@city-and-guilds.co.uk
Website: www.city-and-guilds.co.uk

The Mental Health Foundation
7th Floor
83 Victoria Street
London
SW1H 0HW
Tel: 020 7802 0300
Fax: 020 7802 0301
Email: mhf@mhf.org.uk
Website: www.mentalhealth.org.uk

Mind
15–19 Broadway
London
E15 4BQ
Tel: 020 8519 2122
Fax: 020 8522 1725
Email: contact@mind.org.uk
Website: www.mind.org.uk

National Open College Network (Awarding body)
University of Derby
Kedleston Road
Derby DE22 1GB
Tel: 01332 591071
Email: nocn@nocn.org.uk
Website: www.nocn.org.uk

Rethink
(formerly National Schizophrenic Fellowship)
28 Castle Street
Kingston-Upon-Thames
Surrey KT1 1SS
Tel: 020 8547 3937
Fax: 020 8547 3862
Email: info@rethink.org
Website: www.rethink.org

Richmond Fellowship Head Office
80 Holloway Road
London
N7 8JG
Tel: 020 7697 3300
Fax: 020 7697 3301
Email: enquiries@richmondfellowship.org.uk
Website: www.richmondfellowship.org.uk

The Samaritans
The Upper Mill
Kingston Road
Ewell
Surrey KT17 2AF
Tel: 020 8394 8300
Fax: 020 8394 8301
Email: admin@samaritans.org
Website: www.samaritans.org.uk

UKAN (United Kingdom Advocacy Network)
Volserve House
14-18 West Bar Green
Sheffield
S1 2DA
Tel: 0114 272 8171
Fax: 0114 272 7786
Email: liz@u-kan.co.uk

BILD Services

Information Services provides up to date reading lists, literature searches and a library loan service for BILD members. For more information contact the information department on 01562 723010.

Learning Services provides in house training, distance learning, conferences and workshops. The BILD Certificates Programme can provide accreditation for staff through studying this and other units. For more information call 01562 723025 or email learning@bild.org.uk.

BILD Publications publishes books, training materials and accessible materials for practitioners, parents and other informal carers, and people with learning disabilities. For a free BILD publications catalogue, call 01562 723010 or email t.tindell@bild.org.uk.

BILD Membership. Discounts on training and publications, a free members' handbook and free subscription to the British Journal of Learning Disabilities. For more information, call 01562 723015 or email m.davies@bild.org.uk.

Other titles published by BILD, as part of its programme to support the *Certificates in Working with People who have Learning Disabilities*

Induction: Starting Work with People with Learning Disabilities
Alice Bradley

A study workbook for staff starting a new job with people with learning disabilities, with clear text and illustrations, and work-based activities.

The workbook provides all the information needed for the Induction - Learning Disability unit of the Certificate in Working with People who have Learning Disabilities at Level two*, and covers:

- You and your job
- Confidentiality
- About learning disability
- Lessons from history
- Challenging behaviour.

*Does not cover Induction – safe practitioner.

2001   ISBN 1 902519 80 9   A4   £12.00

Foundation in Care - Understanding Abuse
Foundation in Care - Understanding Positive Communication
Alice Bradley

Two study workbooks for staff in their first six months of working with people with learning disabilities.

Understanding Abuse covers:

- A disabling society
- Recognising abuse
- Recognising neglect
- Power, control and responsibility.

Understanding Positive Communication covers:

- Communication in more than words
- Communication and physical contact
- Communication and challenging behaviour
- Practical strategies to deal with emotional arousal
- Reports, record-keeping and care plans.

By reading through the workbooks, and carrying out the activities, staff will have all the information they need for the Foundation – Understanding Abuse and Understanding Positive Communication unit of the Certificate in Working with People who have Learning Disabilities at Level two.

2001   ISBN 1 902519 89 2 A4   Two units   £20.00

Positive Approaches to Challenging Behaviour
James Hogg and John Harris

A course of six independent study workbooks for staff and first line managers working with people with learning disabilities who present challenging behaviour.

Topics covered include:

- Understanding the origins of challenging behaviour
- Promoting non-challenging behaviour and responding to people who are emotionally aroused.
- Managing challenging behaviour
- Promoting non-challenging behaviour: communication
- Promoting non-challenging behaviour: participation in community life
- Promoting non-challenging behaviour: supporting relationships

The activities throughout the text can be carried out in a variety of care settings, including day and residential services.

Positive Approaches to Challenging Behaviour is fully mapped to units from the Level Two and Level Three Certificates in Working with People who have Learning Disabilities.

2001   ISBN 1 902519 66 3   A4   £60.00 for the set

Mandatory Workbooks
Alice Bradley

Positive Approaches to Anti Oppressive Practice
Positive Approaches to Assessing Care Planning
Positive Approaches to Communication
Positive Approaches to Handling Information
Positive Approaches to Learning Disability
Positive Approaches to Protecting from Abuse
Positive Approaches to Reviewing Care Plans
Positive Approaches to Understanding and Managing Risk

These eight workbooks provide all the information needed for the eight mandatory units of the Learning Disabilities Awards Framework at levels 2 and 3.

Written in a lively and accessible style, with numerous examples and case studies provided by an advisory group of people with learning disabilities, they build on the content of the Induction and Foundation units and can be purchased singly or as a pack.

2002 ISBN 1 904082 09 2 (set of 8) £80.00

To order any of these titles, please contact BILD Publications, Plymbridge Distributors, Estover Road, Plymouth, PL6 7PZ. Tel 01752 202301. Please add 10% for postage and packing for orders under £50 and 5% for orders over £50.00.